Moment by Moment

*The art and
practice of
mindfulness...*

JerryBraza, Ph.D.

Foreword by Thich Nhat Hanh
Nobel Peace Prize nominee

Published by

Healing
Resources
Salt Lake City, Utah

Published by Healing Resources
P.O. Box 9478, Salt Lake City, Utah 84109

ISBN 0-9634863-0-6

*"We can only be said to be alive
in those moments when our hearts
are conscious of our treasures."*

—Thorton Wilder

Table of Contents

Foreword

Foreword

by Thich Nhat Hanh

MINDFULNESS is the basis for transforming ourselves and creating a more harmonious family and society. It is the miracle that allows us to become fully alive in each moment. The deepest fruit of mindfulness practice is the realization that peace and joy are available, within us and around us, right here and now. This is something we can taste, and we can offer it to everyone we meet and everyone we love.

In *Moment by Moment*, Dr. Jerry Braza suggests many simple exercises to apply the practice of mindfulness to our daily lives. I congratulate him for offering such thoughtful, creative, and clear explanations of the practical benefits of practicing mindfulness. This is a very useful guide for living mindfully. I hope you will return to it again and again and practice wholeheartedly the exercises Dr. Braza offers.

> Thich Nhat Hanh
> Plum Village, France
> January 1993

Acknowledgements

This book reflects daily interaction and relationship with family, friends, and, in particular, my wife Kathleen. With her help I have an ongoing opportunity to practice mindfulness *Moment by Moment*. Her love, support, and encouragement have provided a mirror for my own struggle of living mindfully. In addition, she has provided the editorial critique which has kept me focused.

I appreciate my daughter Andrea, and son Mark, who loved me despite my earlier years of "mindless" and "hurried" living. Now as young adults they have provided a validation for my more mindful lifestyle. I appreciate my friends who have offered support and feedback regarding this project, especially Dave Disorbio, whose presence reminds me of the mindfulness process. My editor Becky Jones, once again, has displayed her skill and compassion in helping to facilitate the publication of this book. Special thanks to Toni Mertin at Simply Design for her artistic and organizational efforts which provided an appealing final product.

I also acknowledge my mother, Genevieve, who mindfully watches the apple tree bloom, produce, and shed its leaves outside her apartment window. Mom, thanks for all the moments that you shared with me and for your ongoing love and support.

*I*ntroduction

Introduction

You are about to discover, and hopefully begin to experience, one of the oldest and most profound strategies for enhancing health, relationships, productivity, and happiness—*Mindfulness.*

Mindfulness is a process of becoming fully aware of each moment and one's experience of that moment. Rooted in ancient traditions, this practice is being used successfully today at mind-body clinics nationwide.

Early in my life, I tended to live for the next moment. I was the type of individual who would skip pages when reading bedtime stories to my children. My idea of a family vacation was "getting there," and seldom was the process very enjoyable. Through meditation (which simply means "to attend to"), I began to transform my way of looking at life. My experience has been that most people tend to enjoy life less because they often "miss it" along the way. Life is everything we miss while we are making other plans.

After a critical review of the literature in the field of health and psychology, I discovered literally hundreds of different strategies for achieving well-being and happiness. However, it became clear to me that no single technique or process is the "magic pill" for managing stress or the other life problems we experience. Consequently, I became more interested in exploring the philosophies and approaches that can help individuals live more fully, both at home and in the work place. I invite you to consider the *quality* of your experience "moment by moment" as a practical and even unique barometer of a healthy and successful life. The practice of **Mindfulness** is one way to begin this adventure.

The materials in this book are based on the **Mindfulness Training Program** that I have created and conducted for individuals from various professions who want to experience life more fully. The program is the result of my experiences with teachers like Carl Rogers, who taught me the value of *presence;* Elisabeth Kübler-Ross, who impressed upon me the importance of completing unfinished business; Beata Jencks, who stressed awareness and breathing in her mind-body work; Ram Dass, Stephen Levine, and Jack Kornfield, who introduced me to the practice of meditation; and especially Thich Nhat Hanh, who continues to inspire me with his mindful presence, teachings, and on-going contributions to individual and world peace.

This is not just another book on managing stress, although mindfulness provides a fundamental way of coping with that problem. My goal is to help you recall what you already know and reawaken your spirit to the beauty and joy that exists in every moment.

Moment by Moment can become a tool that helps you learn how to regain that natural state of joy and discovery so recognizable in a young child, that state of appreciation for each moment as it is experienced for the first time. Learning to become more mindful provides an alternative to living *mindlessly* or mechanically.

Moment by Moment can also remind you of the preciousness of each moment and help you realize that the next moment could possibly be your last. This book offers a process and applications that can help you experience the most routine activities—such as breathing, eating, and walking—with joy. This process can literally become a *way of being* that can reduce stress, enhance productivity and relationships, and create joy. The reader is encouraged to use this book as a companion and guide to mindful living. Take time to pause, reflect, and practice the exercises along the way. **Learning "to be" is as important as learning "to do."**

Right now, in this moment, pause and appreciate your breath and aliveness. In this moment, there is health, wholeness, and the potential for joy and peace. Through this simple awareness of your breath and the present moment, you have already begun a process that hopefully you will learn to practice and experience *moment by moment.*

As we begin this journey into *Mindfulness,* I invite you to reflect upon the following questions. These questions can only be answered by looking deeply within yourself, a process addressed throughout this book.

1. What am I missing while I am making other plans?
2. Where am I going anyway?
3. How would I complete the following statements?
   "I'll be happy when _____."
   "If only _____."
4. What from the past is robbing me of a sense of peace?
5. How often am I *with* someone, yet not really there?
6. How often do I live in the present moment?
7. What keeps me from living in the present moment?
8. What pleasurable things am I attached to?
9. What painful things do I deny?
10. What am I "hanging on" to?
11. What pleasures have I failed to enjoy?
12. What are the optimum conditions for my personal growth?
13. In what ways can I become more peaceful?
14. Who are the happiest people I know?
15. What is their secret?
16. What kind of experiences/activities provide me with the greatest joy?
17. In what moments of my life am I most alive?
18. Am I a "human **doing**" or a "human **being**?"
19. What are the optimum conditions for really being with another person?

A "core question" is the question or issue of greatest relevance to an individual. From the list above, select your own core question and write it below:

Moment by Moment offers insights regarding these and many more questions that pertain to living one's life in a more mindful and awakened way.

PART ONE:

An Overview

In Part One, you will:

❖ Discover the meaning of mindfulness

❖ Develop a "mind-set" for developing mindfulness

❖ Learn the importance of mindfulness in your life

❖ Take the Mindfulness Test

❖   ❖   ❖

*Mindfulness is experiencing the body, mind, and spirit
in the same place at the same time.*
—Jerry Braza

❖   ❖   ❖

*I have learned to be happy where I am.
I have learned that locked within the moments of
each day are all the joys, the peace,
the fibers of the cloth we call life....
The meaning is in the moment. There is no other way
to find it. You feel what you allow yourself to feel,
each and every moment of the day.*
—Russ Berrie

What is Mindfulness?

MINDFULNESS is a natural state of living moment by moment. Observe young children, and you will quickly notice that the majority of their awareness is in the present moment. They are not concerned with past or future. This awareness is also observed in the elderly or individuals who are close to death. Recognition of the preciousness of each moment is more apparent in those who know that they are terminal. Although we do not always realize it, we are all terminal!

Mindfulness has many definitions, some of which go back thousands of years:

> *Mindfulness means seeing how things are, directly and immediately seeing for one's self that which is present and true.*
> —Joseph Goldstein

> *Mindfulness refers to keeping one's consciousness alive to the present reality. It is the miracle by which we master and restore ourselves.*
> —Thich Nhat Hanh

> *Mindfulness is an ancient Asian technique, dating back to classical Buddhism in India. It is still practiced in its early form in certain countries, particularly Burma and Thailand. For centuries, the Japanese started to apply Zen awareness to tea-making, proof of how mindfulness can be used in daily routines. Currently, mindfulness is being used as a healing tool in Western medicine.*
> —Daniel Goleman and Tara Bennett-Goleman

> *In the Western traditions, mindfulness is associated with devotional practices in which the Divine is a constant companion within us. In Christianity, the practice is having Jesus by our side at all times. In Judaism, the cabalistic idea that creation is taking place in each and every moment brings an acute sensitivity to everything. All of these ideas can be practiced to raise our level of awareness and induce an entirely new perspective, seeing things "as they really are."*
> —David Cooper

Mindfulness is a technique that teaches intent alertness. It means becoming fully aware of each moment and your activity in that moment. It is living each moment, in contrast to "mindlessness," which means that you allow your mind to get "hooked" or attached to thoughts and desires that arise at random.

Does any of this sound familiar to you? Although you may not have called it mindfulness, the concept is similar to contemplation, prayer, meditation, or the practice of martial arts or yoga, to name a few. All of these practices are based on attention. Growing up Catholic, I practiced repetitive prayers in what is called "saying the rosary." Later, I experimented with a variety of Eastern meditative practices. Through these experiences, I often found serenity and peace in the moment. Although it may merely be a question of semantics, the ingredients of mindfulness are found in most religious traditions and practices.

In general, meditation is based on attention to the workings of the mind, whereas prayer is based on attention to the presence of the sacred in life. According to Rick Fields in *Chop Wood, Carry Water*, "The martial arts, Hatha Yoga, and spiritual dance are based on attention to spirit moving through the body. And the disciplines of inner guidance are based on attention to the wisdom of the 'still, small voice within.'" A common theme in all of these practices is mindfulness.

Mind-set for Mindfulness

Developing mindfulness, like any new behavior, requires a different mind-set. Jon Kabat-Zinn, founder of the University of Massachusetts Medical Center's Stress Reduction Clinic, advocates seven attitudinal foundations of mindfulness: "They are non-judging, patience, a beginner's mind, trust, non-striving, acceptance, and letting go." To help you develop a mind-set for mindfulness, consider the following:

❖ Are you able to observe your thoughts without judging? How often do you judge yourself rather than simply observe the thoughts as they arise? Learning to be unconditional of others begins with being **non-judgmental** of yourself.

❖ Do you seek instant pain relief and instant pleasure, rather than allowing events to occur at their own pace and time? A complete openness to each moment requires **patience.**

❖ Do you consider yourself an "expert" or a "beginner?" From Zen philosophy comes the notion of the **"beginner's mind,"** which means that you are learning to experience each moment and activity as if it were for the first time. Children provide excellent models of this concept.

❖ How often do you wait for others to decide before making a personal decision? Learning to **trust** yourself rather than looking to others is a key to developing mindfulness. In the process of observing thoughts, feelings, sensations, and bodily experiences, you learn to trust that as everything in nature changes, so will the experience of the moment change.

❖ Most of our waking day is spent in "doing" or striving to go somewhere or get something. **Non-striving** infers "being," and striving infers "doing." Creating some time each day to just "be" is difficult, since most of our identity is often based on what we do or what gets done. Developing a proper mind-set for mindfulness requires an awareness of being open to anything and everything that is experienced. Learning to be happy in the moment and finding a time to "be" each day is at the heart of the mindfulness practice.

❖ Do you have a hard time accepting yourself? In practicing mindfulness, you accept each moment as it comes, and you are "with it" fully. **Acceptance** is learned as you observe the thoughts, feelings, sensations, and experiences that arise without judgement.

❖ How often do you "hang on" to experiences and people from the past? Forgiveness means **"letting go."** One of my favorite quotes is, "Hanging on to resentment is allowing someone you despise to live rent free in your head." If you can observe and let go of the thoughts, feelings, sensations, and experiences that arise from moment to moment, it will be easier to let go of the past.

As you progress with the practice of mindfulness, you will learn to personalize what mindfulness means to you and apply this mind-set to your daily practice and interactions.

Reflections

❖ ❖ ❖ ❖ ❖ ❖ ❖

To live without mindfulness is to live as if we were dead already.
—Sharon Salzberg

In the beginner's mind there are many possibilities,
but in the expert's, there are few.
—Shunryu Suzuki

You don't have to do anything. Nowhere to go, nothing to do.
Be peaceful with the way things are now, relax, let go.
—Anonymous

For everything there is a season,
And a time for every matter under heaven:
A time to be born, and a time to die,
A time to kill, and a time to heal,
A time to weep, and a time to laugh;
A time to mourn, and a time to dance,
A time to keep, and a time to cast away...
—Ecclesiastes

I have learned that my total organismic sensing of a situation
is more trustworthy than my intellect.
—Carl Rogers

❖ What does the word mindfulness mean to you?

❖ Allow yourself time to focus on thoughts as they arise. How many are based on judgment?

❖ In what ways in your daily life might you use the concepts described in "Mind-set for Mindfulness?"

Why Mindfulness?

To live each moment as if it were our first and our last may itself provide enough motivation to be mindful. With such awareness, a person clearly sees the present moment as it really is and experiences the beauty that exists. But mindfulness offers even more benefits.

Stress reduction. Sixty to ninety percent of all illness may be directly or indirectly related to stress, and stress reduction is a major concern in our personal and professional lives. Often stress is the result of being over-committed and the tendency in most people to always hurry. Living in the moment may clearly be one of the best-kept secrets for effective stress reduction and wellness. According to a family practice physician, "When the waiting room and all the examining rooms are full, my best coping strategy is to become completely mindful of the person I am with. "

Increased productivity. Effectiveness and productivity are en-hanced when a person's concentration is improved. When the mind wanders, it is difficult to concentrate. Preoccupation with the past or the future, coupled with "polyphasic thinking" (many thoughts), results in unfulfilled activities, tasks, and relationships. Studies have shown that by developing mindfulness, individuals can concentrate more effectively and thus be more productive.

Enhanced relationships. Think about the most important people in your life and recall the last interactions you had with them. Were you really *with* them? See yourself relating to them in more mindful ways in the future. Whether personally or professionally, our presence speaks louder than words. A nursing supervisor recently realized that as she interacted with her colleagues, she was usually working on charting and other tasks at the same time. By truly being present and attentive, you let the other person know that he or she is most important in that moment.

Joy. In our attempts to hurry, we frequently miss the opportunity to enjoy the little pleasures that are happening moment by moment. How many sunsets, smiles, and small adventures have you missed?

As you develop the skill and art of mindfulness, you can learn to work and play in a less frantic, more enjoyable, and more focused manner. As a result, personal relationships are enhanced and more joyful. Overall, being mindful helps us to let go of the past and be less fearful of the future. With this philosophy, we are in the process of healing in the present moment!

Reflections

❖ ❖ ❖ ❖ ❖ ❖ ❖

*Nothing can be more useful to a man or woman than
a determination not to be hurried.*
—Anonymous

The best gift we can give to one another is our presence!
—Jerry Braza

The flower, the sky, your beloved can only be found in the present moment.
—Thich Nhat Hanh

Most men pursue pleasure with such breathless haste, they hurry past it.
—Sören Kierkegaard

❖ Think of one stressful problem in your life today. How might the practice of mindfulness help to reduce the distress (negative consequences) of the problem?

❖ Explore areas in your life in which you are not as productive as you would like. How might the practice of mindfulness enhance your concentration and productivity in your work/personal life?

❖ Think of one person that you often take for granted. How might the practice of mindfulness bring new vitality to that relationship?

❖ What joyful moments in your life can you be sure to capture today?

ᒪ*Mindfulness Test*

Barriers to Mindfulness

To explore the concept of mindfulness, circle your response to the following questions, which reflect some common barriers or blocks to mindfulness.

1. Do I suffer from "hurry sickness?"   YES or NO
   *This is a societal tendency to feel rushed
   and harried even when it is not necessary.*

2. Do I measure happiness by future gains
   and events?   YES or NO
   *Evidence of this includes a preoccupation
   with thoughts such as, "I'll be happy when ... ,"
   "If only ...."*

3. Do I constantly compare the present
   to the past?   YES or NO
   *This is the result of difficulty in letting go
   of experiences from the past such as youth,
   summer, relationships, and so on.*

4. Do I normally try to deny or push
   away pain?   YES or NO
   *This is indicative of an unwillingness to
   confront the negative in your life.*

5. Do I have unfinished business in my life?   YES or NO
   *This relates to unexpressed feelings for
   significant people in your life and/or
   unfulfilled tasks or goals.*

6. Am I often bored with routines and normal day-to-day living?   YES or NO
   Does life seem dull, and do I often say, "Another day of the same old thing"?

7. Am I preoccupied with expectations about the future?   YES or NO

Note: Your responses to these questions provide an indication of your tendency to be mindful. If you responded **YES** to most of these questions, you may **not** be living as mindfully as you could.

Reflections

❖　❖　❖　❖　❖　❖　❖

The past is to be learned from and not lived in, and the future is to be planned for, not paralyzed by, and the present is to be enjoyed right now.
—Anonymous

I have a choice: to rush or be present.
—Jerry Braza

We live in a "state of internal wanting"—return to the experience at the moment as it was for the first time.
—Robert Frost

Comparisons and expectations are "twin thieves" that rob us of the present.
—Jerry Braza

❖ Reflect on how often your model of the past does not
   work for you in the present.

❖ What painful things do you refuse to look at in your
   life today?

❖ What is robbing you of a sense of peace today?

❖ What expectations regarding the future are you willing
   to give up for happiness now?

PART TWO:

*P*rocess

In Part Two, you will:

❖ Develop a technique of mindful breathing

❖ Develop a process for observing the mind and body

❖ Experience the mindfulness process

❖   ❖   ❖

The purpose of the technique is not to lock into the breath,
but to use the breath as a means of tuning to the present.
—Stephen Levine

❖   ❖   ❖

When we are capable of stopping, we begin to see.
—Thich Nhat Hanh

❖   ❖   ❖

Awareness in itself is healing.
—Fritz Pearls

Mindful Breathing

Mindfulness training begins with a focus on breathing. Mindful breathing can result in physical and mental equilibrium and inner harmony. Breathing is a mediator between the body and the mind, connecting the conscious and unconscious.

Most people breathe 17,000–24,000 breaths per day, yet few of us are aware of even one of those breathing cycles. Every moment our breath can create balance within us and bring us back to the present. Everything in nature rises, falls, and exists. In the same way, inhalation is a rising, exhalation a falling, and the pause in between is the existing. Recognize each breath and learn to use breathing as a metaphor for life and the balance that exists in all of nature.

Many individuals have developed poor breathing habits. Males are often told not to cry or to be emotional; consequently, their feelings are often blocked and their breathing is impaired. Both men and women are told that to look "good"—"keep your stomach in and chest out." Once again, proper breathing is impaired. Babies breathe naturally (abdominally). Watch a baby breathe. They are not concerned with how they look. The only time they switch to chest breathing is when they are hungry or feeling discomfort. Likewise, as we become aware of our breathing, we will naturally slow our breath and breathe more abdominally or diaphragmatically.

Becoming mindful of breathing provides many benefits. First, the breath becomes a reminder to come back to the present moment. Often a person will literally pause to catch their breath during a moment of activity or excitement. In such a moment, simply observe your breathing and notice how this practice immediately offers a moment to center yourself and literally refocus mind, body, and spirit. One derivation of the word respiration is to "re-spirit." Use of your breath to center and re-spirit yourself is the core of mindfulness practice.

Breathing helps to provide a moment of rest and renewal. Within each breathing cycle is an opportunity to relax, especially during the exhalation phase of the breath. Notice that as you inhale, you become more energized, and as you exhale, you become more relaxed. During periods of lethargy and sleepiness, awareness of the inhalation of the breath will provide the oxygen needed to restore the body. It may be more helpful than a caffeine drink. Also, during high stress times, such as work pressures, traffic jams, and relationship difficulties, an awareness of the exhalation or relaxation phase of the breath can bring the body back into balance.

Finally, breathing offers one of the best ways to "quiet the mind." A focus on breathing takes one's attention away from a preoccupation with our thinking. As William James said, "The greatest weapon against stress is our ability to choose one thought over another." In this moment, as you bring your full awareness to your breathing, you probably are not thinking about other concerns.

Learning to become aware of and observe your breathing is one of the best ways to become mindful. As you will discover, an awareness of the breath makes it easier to focus on the moment, restore yourself, and quiet the mind. Rediscover for yourself the positive influence that breathing has on your own sense of balance and control. The Latin word for breath is *spiritus*. Allow your breath to flow through you as a sense of spirit flows through your body.

Mindful Breathing Practice

1. Find a comfortable sitting position, with your back straight. Relax your hands and arms, or place them in your lap. Once you have learned this exercise, you may choose to keep your eyes open or closed.

2. Bring your awareness to your breath. Do not change your breathing, but simply observe and experience the in-and-out of your breath at your nose or the rising and falling of your diaphragm. Connect the in-breath to the out-breath, the out-breath to the in-breath.

Note: To help you stay focused, repeat phrases and/or words to help stay focused on the breath. For example:

Breathing in, I know that I am breathing in. (In)

Breathing out, I know that I am breathing out. (Out)*

or

Aware of my body, I breathe in. (Body)

Relaxing my body, I breathe out. (Relaxing)*

After repeating such phrases several times, you may simply say "In" or "Body" on the inhalation, and "Out" or "Relaxing" on the exhalation. Repetition of phrases and words simply helps you keep your focus on the breath and enjoy the present moment. Creating your own phrases or words may give more meaning to your practice.

3. You will naturally become aware of thoughts, senses, feelings, and bodily sensations. As you do, simply become aware of them and then bring your attention back to your breath.

*Verses from Thich Nhat Hanh, learned at Plum Village retreat

Reflections

❖   ❖   ❖   ❖   ❖   ❖   ❖

Our breath is the bridge from our body to our mind.
—Thich Nhat Hanh

*Watch breath, soften belly, open heart, has become a wake-up call for
mindfulness and mercy, which takes people beyond the mind-body
of suffering into the deep peace of their healing.*
—Stephen Levine

Life starts with a breath and ends with a breath.
—Yogi Bhajan

*Breathing in, I calm body and mind. Breathing out, I smile.
Dwelling in the present moment, I know this is the only moment.*
—Thich Nhat Hanh

❖   Identify a time or times in which you will be able to
practice mindful breathing on a daily basis.

❖   In what situations in your personal world might you use
breathing to come back to the present moment, to renew
yourself, and to quiet your mind?

Mindfulness Process

Learning to be mindful is often sabotaged by various interruptions and distractions. For example, how many times do you find yourself at work thinking about the weekend? Or, how many times are you relaxing on the weekend but preoccupied with thoughts of work? The mind naturally pays attention to thoughts, feelings, sensations, and experiences. Thoughts often provoke worry about the past and anxiety about the future. Feelings may arise which are pleasant, unpleasant, or neutral. The senses are constantly providing stimuli through our sight, hearing, taste, smell, and touch. Finally, our bodies are in a state of constant flux with physiological changes that affect muscular tension, breathing rate, comfort, pain, and many other bodily processes.

To more fully understand and work with the typical interruptions and distractions to mindfulness, find a comfortable place to sit where you will be free of distractions for whatever period of time you have available. Begin the "mindful breathing process." With your awareness focused on the in-and-out of your breath, begin—without judgement and with patience—to explore your thoughts, senses, feelings, and bodily experiences as if you were a "beginner" attempting to learn more about yourself.

Thoughts—What are you thinking now? What kind of thoughts are most frequent? Count thoughts as if you were counting trees, sheep, or money. Note the beginning of a thought, its middle, and then follow the thought to its end. "Thoughts and small children have one thing in common: they need attention." Recognize what happens to your thoughts as you simply notice and label each one as "thinking," and then return to your breath.

Sensing—Life is an accumulation of the sensory experiences that we have moment by moment. Our ability to become aware of our senses is one of the most basic ways to experience life fully. Seeing, hearing, tasting, smelling, and touching make up the primary senses.

Look around you—what are you **seeing**? Notice every sound from within your body and your surroundings—what are you **hearing**? What are you **smelling** at this moment? "Braille" your immediate environment: what are you experiencing while **touching**? Find your favorite food and slowly eat it; what do you notice as you are **tasting**? Notice and label *what* you are sensing and how you are sensing it (e.g., label the sound of wind as "hearing," or the sight of a beautiful flower as "seeing"). In this moment, experience the sensation fully, and then return to your breath.

Feeling—Thoughts and sensations create within us a variety of feelings that are pleasant, unpleasant, or neutral. Pleasant feelings, such as joy, gratitude, and peacefulness, often enhance the mindfulness process. It is easy to be present for exciting and happy moments. Unpleasant feelings, such as anger and sadness, are most often avoided. Neutral feelings are typical during times of boredom or periods during which nothing pleasant or unpleasant arises. Notice what you are feeling in this moment. Are your feelings pleasant, unpleasant, or neutral? What specific feelings are you experiencing? Notice and label what you are feeling at this moment, experience the sensation fully, and return to your breath.

Bodily Experiences—Every moment lived in awareness offers information regarding changes going on within our bodies. Note for a moment how your breathing changes. Recognize areas of discomfort or pain, which are often noticed through an awareness of muscular tension. Become aware of temperature shifts of warmth and cold in various parts of the body. What are you experiencing in your body at this moment? Notice and label what you are experiencing in this moment (e.g., label tightness in the neck and shoulders as "tension"), experience the sensation fully, and return to your breath.

Through this process you have expanded your awareness and enhanced your mindfulness. Beauty exists all around us, even in the people and places we don't like. In becoming more aware, we are literally coming to our senses!

Mindfulness requires a time each day for practice. Coming back to the present moment is enhanced by an awareness of your purpose, attention, and breathing. First, begin by focusing on your breathing as described earlier. During daily practice sessions, your purpose is to focus on your breath. Eventually, learn to apply mindfulness to every moment of your life. To practice and enhance mindfulness in daily life, the following process is helpful.

1. **What is my purpose in this moment?**

   (For example, during your daily practice, use focusing on your breath as your purpose. Other purposes you can use include such activities as completing a report, talking to a patient/client, or reading a bedtime story to your child.) *What am I here for? Returning to your purpose in the moment offers a focus for your practice.*

2. **When your mind wanders, stop and observe: in this moment, where is my awareness or attention?**

   What am I thinking?
   (about the past or future, planning, worrying)

   What am I sensing?
   (seeing, hearing, tasting, smelling, touching)

   What am I feeling?
   (pleasant, unpleasant, neutral)

   What am I experiencing in my body?
   (tension, calm, tightness)

   Simply note your thinking, sensing, feeling, or whatever you are experiencing in your body.

3. Bring your awareness/attention back to the moment and your purpose by breathing in and breathing out.

   Do not attempt to change your breathing, but merely observe and experience the in-and-out of your breath and return to your purpose in the moment.

4. **Repeat these steps as necessary to bring yourself back to the moment.**

   A good way to apply this process is to practice it daily and use breathing as the focal point (purpose) for the mindfulness process. Finding a quiet place and consistent time helps develop this process, which can slowly be applied to all activities, experiences, and interactions.

Reflections

❖　❖　❖　❖　❖　❖　❖

A famous meditation teacher was once asked, "How long do you meditate each day?" The reply was, "Formally, for several hours per day I sit and meditate, and informally I meditate all day long, with every activity becoming the focus of my meditation."
—Anonymous

If mindfulness refers to keeping one's consciousness alive to the present reality, then one must practice right now in one's daily life, not only during meditation sessions.
—Thich Nhat Hanh

Mindfulness is the practice of aiming your attention, moment by moment, in the direction of your purpose. It is called mindfulness, because you have to keep your purpose in mind as you watch your attention. Then, whenever you notice that your aim has drifted off purpose, you calmly realign it.
—Frank Andrews

❖ Explore ways in which awareness might be helpful in healing yourself and your relationships.

❖ In what circumstances, both personally and professionally, might you apply the mindfulness process to your life?

PART THREE:

Application of Mindfulness

In Part Three, you will learn to:

❖   Manage stress

❖   Quiet the mind

❖   Transform difficult feelings

❖   Enhance concentration and productivity

❖   Deepen relationships

❖   Complete unfinished business

❖   Experience daily activities mindfully

*If you are at all successful in developing this type of detached witnessing
(it does take time), you will be able to look upon the events occurring
in your mind-and-body with the very same impartiality that you
would look upon clouds floating through the sky, water rushing in a stream,
rain cascading on a roof, or any other objects in your field of awareness.*
—Ken Wilber

*Life is filled with suffering, but it is also filled with many wonders,
like the blue sky, the sunshine, the eyes of a baby. To suffer is not enough.
We must also be in touch with the wonders of life.
They are within us and all around us, everywhere, any time.*
—Thich Nhat Hanh

*Don't look to the past in anger nor the future in fear,
but around in awareness.*
—James Thurber

Managing Stress

Stress is both a normal psychological and physiological response to events in our life. This response is innate and is often a means of self-preservation. Conversely, *distress* is often the result of our *interpretation* of the events in our life. Epictetus, a first century Roman philosopher, makes this clear with his statement, "Man is not disturbed by events, but by the view he takes of them." Thus, any event in our life can be labeled as stress or distress based upon our interpretation or, even more significant, our *judgment*, of the particular event.

Famous transpersonal psychologist, Ken Wilber notes, "If we can watch or witness our distress, we prove ourselves thereby to be 'distressless,' free of the witnessed turmoil." Exploring that process may provide an understanding of how both mindfulness and becoming familiar with the "witness" within us can help reduce the potential negative psychological and physical impact of events in our lives.

Distress begins with a simple thought, but years later may become a piece of "unfinished business" that reduces our potential for experiencing peace, joy, and happiness. The "anatomy of distress" essentially unfolds as follows:

1. **Awareness/consciousness** occurs when you see, hear, smell, taste, experience, and/or think in response to a recollection or a direct contact with some object, person, activity, and/or environment.

    (e.g., as you enjoy your gardening, you become aware of—conscious of—a project at work)

2. **Feelings then arise which are pleasant, unpleasant, and/or neutral.**

    (e.g., the thought of the project is unpleasant)

3. **Perceptions and reasoning begins to occur.** Most often, an evaluation or judgment is made.

   (e.g., this project is unpleasant, difficult, and you think you should be putting in extra work time now, instead of gardening)

4. **Distorted and exaggerated thinking** often follows the judgment or evaluation. This kind of thinking most often has roots in *wants, desires,* our *concept* or *perception of self,* and the *views and opinions* (models) we often attach to one way of thinking, being, or doing.

   (e.g., "What's wrong with me? Why is this project so hard for me and not for Joe? I shouldn't be enjoying gardening when I have more important things to do.")

5. **Distorted and/or exaggerated thinking continues.** Now you become focused or "caught" on the problem, and this often creates *distress* by continuing to attach various judgmental thoughts, ("should's" and "ought-to's") feelings, and bodily sensations to the experience.

   (e.g., your preoccupation with the problem continues all weekend. You worry constantly, have trouble sleeping, and feel bad. Based on this exaggerated thinking, you have been negatively affected mentally and physically)

Exploring this model can help us understand how a simple thought can create suffering/distress. Learning to become mindful or to simply "witness" the scenario as it unfolds can be a powerful way of changing potentially distressful situations. For example, by becoming mindful at the very moment in which unpleasant thoughts arise (e.g., the project at work), you can simply note and/or witness the thought

("Hmm…a *work* thought") before exaggerated thinking or judgments become the focal point of your awareness. By applying the mindfulness practice to any stressful situation, you learn to *"witness"* rather than react.

Several years ago, my wife and I had planned a ten-day vacation to the Garden Island of Kauai, Hawaii. For months we reviewed the brochures, and talked with travel agents and friends who had vacationed there before. Daily we talked about our trip—time to walk on the beach, rounds of golf, snorkeling, and the whale watching trips. Soon the big day arrived, we left the cold and smoggy winter weather of Salt Lake City and flew to sunny Hawaii.

Upon arrival, we were greeted by torrential rains that we thought were temporary. Day after day the rain continued, and our outlook dimmed. All the things we had planned to do for months were cancelled day by day as the storm continued. The model that we created in our minds regarding Hawaii was not to be fulfilled. In our preoccupation with what we wanted to experience, we missed truly experiencing the rain, and, I suspect, many wonderful relaxing moments. For ten days, we became more and more depressed since our expectations were not met. Having rigid views and opinions (models) regarding any event or experience creates unnecessary stress. Learning to truly "witness" and not be "attached" to wants, desires, views, and opinions allows you to be free to make choices and create new and exciting experiences.

You may be familiar with accounts of individuals who have had a "near-death" or "out-of-body" experience. These individuals often "witness" their trauma and the accompanying resuscitation attempts from unusual and unique vantage points, without feeling or attachment to the event. You need not have a near-death or out-of-body experience to also become a "witness" to events in your life!

Reflections

❖　❖　❖　❖　❖　❖　❖

Pain is inevitable; suffering is optional.
—Anonymous

Thus, as we begin to touch the transpersonal witness,
we begin to let go of our purely personal problems, worries,
and concerns. For our only concern here is to watch our
particular distresses, to simply and innocently be aware of them,
without judging them, avoiding them, dramatizing them, working on them.
—Ken Wilber

Every act, however small, can teach you everything,
provided you see who it is that is acting.
—Thomas Merton

Thus, ultimately to try to escape a distress merely perpetuates that distress.
What is so upsetting is not the distress itself, but our attachment to that
distress. We identify with it, and that alone is the real difficulty.
—Ken Wilber

❖　When you find yourself involved in a stressful situation,
begin to "witness" the in-and-out of your breath. Stop
and observe: in this moment, where is my awareness or
attention? Witness and label your *thinking, sensing, feeling*
and *bodily experience.* Bring your awareness/attention
back to the moment by breathing in and out. The key is
to witness what is causing the distress. By simply becoming an impartial observer, separate and unattached, you
soon realize that the distress is simply caused by thoughts,
feelings, senses, or bodily experiences. In learning to
"witness," you begin to see yourself as an outside observer. The next time you have a headache, for example,
try the "witnessing" process to help "detach" yourself not
only from the pain, but, perhaps, the source of the pain
as well.

Quieting the Mind

Two major sources of stress are the mind and the way in which we interpret every situation in our lives. Our bodies respond physiologically to the thoughts that we hang on to (past or future thinking) or that result from distorted thinking. Most people are troubled with such thoughts at bedtime or in the middle of the night. Insomnia is a common complaint often aggravated by distorted thinking and a preoccupation with the past or future.

Living in the present is difficult when you have a lot on your mind. Most stress originates from our thoughts of the past or concerns about the future. How many times have you become preoccupied with the potential disasters of some event in the future, only to realize when the time finally arrived that most of your worrying was in vain?

Clearly, it is important to plan for the future, but not to be obsessed with its outcome. In planning, it is human nature to consider all possible negative consequences, or the so-called "worst-case scenario." However, according to cognitive therapists, the mind has a tendency to create distortions, referred to as "cognitive distortions" or "distorted thinking." All these distortions and preoccupations with the past or the future become invitations to live outside the present moment. But more significantly, these thoughts become the basis for stress and anxiety. Learning to quiet the mind is the basis for becoming more mindful and open to the beauty surrounding us.

There are many techniques for quieting the mind. Most techniques use a word or phrase (e.g., Christian meditations may use "Jesus," "Lord," etc.) or object(s) (e.g., counting sheep, focusing on a candle's flame), which provide a distraction. An example is the Centering Prayer, developed by Basil Pennington, a Catholic priest. He describes this prayer "in a general sense to refer to any method by which the pray-er seeks to bring his or her scattered thoughts and feelings together to allow for a certain deepening." This prayer focuses on a simple word such as "Jesus." The chosen word may vary and it often spontaneously arises and is based on faith and love and one's relationship to God in that moment. You can vary the word daily, but you repeat it to yourself and return to the word whenever you become aware of anything else.

The following "quieting the mind" technique is similar to the basic mindfulness process, with emphasis placed on labeling thoughts. This strategy may be helpful for those who have difficulty falling asleep or at any time when one is preoccupied with certain thoughts.

Quieting the Mind—Basic Practice

Since most distress relates to a preoccupation with thoughts, practice observing these thoughts and then "letting go" of them.

1. Begin to focus on your breath at the tip of your nostrils or on the rising and falling of the abdomen. Keep your attention on the breath.

2. Naturally, thoughts will enter your consciousness. Use your thoughts as the object of relaxation or meditation. As thoughts arise in your mind, simply become aware of them and note the general nature of your thinking, or label the thought as one of *hunger, pain, sleep, sex,* etc.

3. Bring your attention back to your breath. When you are aware of the thought, it loses some of its power. Do not resist the thought, since "what you resist persists." Stress and tension develop as we become preoccupied with certain thoughts.

Reflections

❖ ❖ ❖ ❖ ❖ ❖ ❖

*Worrying about the future is like trying to eat the hole
in a doughnut. It's munching on what isn't.*
—Barry Neil Kaufman

*The trouble with Archie is he don't know how
to worry without getting upset.*
—Edith Bunker on sitcom "All in the Family"

*The fact that the mind rules the body is, in spite of its neglect by
biology and medicine, the most fundamental fact which
we know about the process of life.*
—Franz Alexander, M.D.

❖ Can you identify situations in which you would be able
   to use the "quieting the mind" technique? The technique
   was helpful to me at several points while writing this
   book. I discovered that my thoughts about getting my
   work to the editor would get in the way of clarifying a
   point or staying with the theme of the present chapter.
   By taking a moment to label my thought ("hurry
   thought") and to breathe, I could quickly bring myself
   back to the task at hand.

❖ Using the "beginner's mind," take some time to explore
   the nature of your thoughts. Note the beginning and
   ending of each thought, recognize the types of thoughts
   you are experiencing, and witness how thoughts are only
   thoughts.

Transforming Feelings

Stress is often created when we are preoccupied with thoughts and feelings. Feelings in particular can create a vicious cycle of thinking that leads to pleasant, unpleasant, and neutral states. There are many ways to cope with feelings, such as physical activity and forms of cognitive therapy. However, mindfulness can also help us cope with or transform our feelings.

Transforming Feelings—Basic Technique

To transform a feeling, begin with mindful breathing. Focus on your breath at the tip of your nostrils or the abdomen. Keep your attention on the breath flowing in and out. Naturally, thoughts will enter your consciousness and may lead to a feeling state, such as anger. As that feeling enters your consciousness, simply become aware of it, and then bring your attention back to your breath. Through a simple awareness of the feeling, it loses some of its power. In this moment, accept the feeling. Do not resist. Embrace it. Befriend the anger and become one with it. As you breathe in and breathe out, observe and study the anger. Begin to calm the anger through your mindful breathing and the repetition of verses, such as these phrases used at a retreat led by Thich Nhat Hanh in Plum Village, France:

> *"Experiencing the feeling of anger in me, I breathe in.*
> *Smiling at the feeling of anger in me, I breathe out."*

Preferably, create your own short phrases, and repeat and connect them with each breathing cycle. Examples include:

Breathing in, I recognize my anger.
Breathing out, I am aware of how angry I am.
Breathing in, I see my anger overwhelming me.
Breathing out, I recognize that the anger affects my entire body.

Through continued awareness and a sense of calmness, you will find it becomes easier to change the intensity of the anger and gradually release the anger, letting it go.

If the feeling state is not strong, simply note the feeling during practice and then return your focus to the breath. Through your awareness of the feeling, the intensity of the feeling will change in the same way that nature is constantly changing.

Reflections

❖   ❖   ❖   ❖   ❖   ❖   ❖

You cannot perceive beauty but with a serene mind.
—Henry David Thoreau

I don't express anger, I get a tumor instead.
—Woody Allen

The only way out is through.
—Robert Frost

In order to have real transformation, we have to deal with the roots of our anger. If we don't, the seeds of anger will grow again.
—Thich Nhat Hanh

❖   Think of one feeling that you typically have difficulty with, allow yourself some time to practice the basic technique described in this chapter for transforming feelings. After completing this practice session, take some time to write about your experience. Note how you are feeling in this moment.

Enhancing Concentration & Productivity

As a reformed "Type A" personality (coronary-prone individual who is always in a hurry), I have continually struggled with staying focused and concentrated. Because of my underlying desire to "hurry" and my belief system that later was better than now, concentration was often difficult. I would compensate with hurrying even more and by spending more time than was necessary on personal and professional assignments, jobs, and projects. As I started to practice mindfulness, I found to my surprise that I was able to stay focused longer, and gradually I could work more effectively and successfully.

As you learn the practice of mindfulness and focus on breathing, your quality of concentration can improve. Studies of experienced meditators indicate an ability to stay focused for long periods of time. As we practice the mindfulness process, our greatest distractions result from thoughts, sensations, and feelings that are constantly arising. Through awareness, you can "witness" the distraction without responding to the message. For example, as I write this book, I am often distracted by thoughts such as "take a break," or feelings such as "I don't like doing this now." If I respond to every distraction, it is clear that very little will be accomplished.

In addition to your ongoing mindfulness practice, applying the basic mindfulness process to work projects is an effective way to enhance your productivity. Remember:

Step 1: What is my purpose in this moment?

(e.g., to complete this memo announcing tomorrow's meeting)

Step 2: When your mind wanders, stop and observe: What am I thinking, sensing, feeling, or experiencing?

(e.g., in the process of completing this memo, I am reminded of going home in the rush hour traffic)

Step 3: Simply note your thought, breathe, and bring your attention back to the project.

(e.g., instead of being preoccupied with the traffic, I simply note my thoughts regarding the traffic, and use my breath as a reminder to concentrate on completing the memo)

Other strategies for enhancing your productivity and concentration include:

1. Have a clear purpose and/or goal(s) for the work at hand.

2. Bracket time for each project. Being clear on the amount of time that you have available for each project will add structure to your work. Often when I know that I have 30 minutes to complete a task, I am more likely to stay focused and complete the job in the allotted time.

3. Begin tasks you have a chance of completing. Not only does this help you stay focused, but it also offers the intrinsic rewards found in completion. If the project is multifaceted, divide it by setting mini-goals along the way, and complete each of these in the allotted time.

4. Take time along the way to offer feedback to yourself or others who are working with you on the project. Look at the report you finished or the memo you just wrote, and admire and validate yourself for completing the tasks. In working with others, remember their need for feedback.

Reflections

❖   ❖   ❖   ❖   ❖   ❖   ❖

*If you pay attention at every moment, you form a new
relationship to time... In some magical way, by slowing down,
you become more efficient, productive, and energetic, focusing
without distraction directly on the task in front of you. Not only do
you become immersed in the moment, you become that moment.*
—Michael Ray

*The first landmark in concentration comes when the meditator's mind is
unaffected both by outer distractions, such as nearby sounds, and by the
turbulence of his own assorted thoughts and feelings.*
—Daniel Goleman

❖   Make a list of the most important activities you need
to complete each day to be successful. Now visualize
yourself being mindful during the completion of each
activity. Close your eyes and see yourself entering into a
state of mindfulness as you undertake and complete the
most important projects.

Deepening Relationships

George Bernard Shaw once said, "My tailor is the wisest of persons who comes to see me. Every time he comes, he takes new measurements." How do you enter each interaction and relationship? Are you like the tailor, who looks at each person as if he were seeing that person for the first time? Or do you take other people for granted, because you have previous experience with them and you have already "sized" them up? Do you ever consider that they may have changed or grown since your last interaction? How often do you take people for granted and as a result have failed to be "present" with them?

In both a personal and professional sense, the greatest gift we give to one another is our *presence*. In my work with caregivers, I have realized that one of the most powerful ingredients for enhancing healing and change is presence. Carl Rogers, the father of humanistic psychology, was known for his psychological presence and openness. Clients and colleagues often remarked that his eyes were really seeing them, and his ears were fully taking in their words. In thinking of the people that I enjoy being with, I recognize that the quality which I admire most is their presence, or their willingness to convey to me that in this moment no one else is more important.

Learning to listen to another person becomes the best strategy for enhancing presence. Chogyam Trungpa identifies three kinds of listening that are often destructive to meaningful relationships. In the first kind of listening, one's mind is wandering so much that there is no room at all for anything that's being said—one is just there physically. In the second kind, one's mind is relating somewhat to what's being said, but basically it is still wandering. In the third kind, one's mind contains aggression, jealousy, and destruction of all kinds. One has mixed feelings about what is being said and cannot really understand it (quoted by David Brandon in *Zen in the Art of Helping*). Can you relate to any of these examples? Learning to be present for another requires an ability to let go of thoughts that block true intimacy with that individual.

Learning to listen requires the constant application of the basic mindfulness process discussed earlier in this book. Remember:

Step 1: My purpose at this moment is to be with this person. I use this person as the source of meditation, meaning that I "attend to" him or her.

Step 2: When my presence is distracted, I note the distraction as thinking, sensing, feeling, or experiencing.

Step 3: I become aware of my breathing and bring my attention back to the person.

Repeat these steps whenever you are distracted. The most important person to be with is the person you are with. This ongoing technique lets us provide the best gift we have—our complete self—to each person.

Reflections

❖　❖　❖　❖　❖　❖　❖

Every time we meet is the first time, because every time you are different, as I also am.
We do not step twice in the same river, said Heraclitus;
this was said very truly, as the river flows without end,
and its waters are never the same.
—Carlos Valles

To be truly present with another person, I must find what interests me, what distracts me from my busy inner world, which is flooded with chatter and images.
—Don Hanlon Johnson

❖ Think about the most important people in your life.
Consider applying this strategy of mindfulness to your
next interaction with them. See them as if you were a
tailor, noting everything about them in a new and fresh
way. Practice this with every person you meet, familiar
and unfamiliar. What are the typical distractions which
prevent you from truly *being* with another individual?
Use each person as a reminder to be mindful. How can
you create more mindful moments with those you love?

Completing Unfinished Business

In the process of quieting your mind and becoming more mindful, it is likely that you will become aware of some of your "unfinished business." In addition, your efforts to live mindfully may be hampered by this unfinished business. The famous death and dying specialist, Elisabeth Kübler-Ross, defines unfinished business as "something that is incomplete in our lives that deprives us of a sense of peace." Unfinished business almost always involves relationships and things that have been said or left unsaid, done or not done. It also includes tasks never completed, trips not taken, and dreams and goals not fulfilled.

Completing your own unfinished business allows you to let go of the past and live more fully in the present moment. As you examine your life, your goals, your relationships, what is unfinished? What keeps robbing you of a sense of peace?

Psychologically speaking, all experiences "hang around" until a person can achieve closure with them. Whenever unfinished business forms the center of existence, the mind is hampered. The content of unfinished business and how it is handled are key to living life more fully.

Despite an understanding of unfinished business, many individuals still carry around "baggage" from the past. How do we know that we have unfinished business? Consider the following questions:

❖ Are you preoccupied with the thought of a person or a past experience?

❖ Do you easily cry or get angry at the thought of this person?

❖ Are your thoughts frequently prefaced by, "If only ... ?"

❖ Do you find yourself becoming psychologically bothered and emotionally involved with another person's problems when they are similar to your own problems?

❖　What are you currently "putting off" in your life?

To complete your unfinished business, quiet yourself, breathe, and ponder what you have or haven't said, and what you have or haven't done. To confront your unfinished business, consider your own mortality and use death as an advisor. Ultimately, we are all going to die. Try living each moment as if it were the last one.

It is important to note that sometimes the core of unfinished business is related to early pain and trauma, such as abuse and incest. If your life is continually affected by these experiences, please consider seeking professional assistance.

Reflections

❖　　❖　　❖　　❖　　❖　　❖　　❖

We should live our life like a very hot fire, so there is nothing left behind—everything is burned to a white ash.
—Suzuki Roshi

Two monks are walking along a road, and they come to a river.
On the bank is a beautiful young woman who is afraid to cross the river by herself. One of the monks gallantly steps forth and offers her a ride on his shoulders. Upon reaching the other side, she thanks the monk and they go their separate ways. About one hundred steps down the road, the second monk says to the first, "How could you do that? You are a monk, a renunciate. You should not be carrying beautiful women around on your shoulders."
To which the first monk replied, "Oh, are you still carrying her?
I let her down when we reached the shore."
—Traditional Zen story

❖ If you had only one year to live and could live it in relatively good health, what would you do differently? (How do you know you *don't* have a year to live?)

❖ If you knew you would die tomorrow and could make one telephone call, who would you call? What would you say? What "unfinished business" would be part of your conversation? Make those calls, express those feelings, and take those trips! What are you waiting for?

Experiencing Daily Activities

Mindfulness can become a part of all our daily activities. The following discourses on mindful eating and walking are just two examples of mindfulness applied to our daily lives.

When mindfulness is applied to eating, it becomes a powerful tool that can enhance the joy and beneficial effects of food. We frequently gulp down our meals and combine them with other activities, such as reading the newspaper, watching television, or interacting with the family. Since eating often becomes a secondary experience, its real pleasure is missed. Food that is chewed slowly is easily digested, and you are less likely to overeat when you are mindful or aware.

Mindful Eating Process

1. Before eating, remember your purpose: *to eat.*

2. Before eating, take a moment to become aware of your breathing.

3. Slow down the overall eating process. Chew your food slowly.

4. Involve all of your senses (sight, hearing, taste, smell, touch) in experiencing your meal.

5. As your mind wanders, bring your awareness back to the moment. Eating is the object of your attention.

Think how often eating is a completely "mindless" activity. Learn to break the habitual cycle, which generally includes a lack of awareness and a need to hurry. By becoming mindful, you will find that eating becomes a more pleasing and fulfilling experience. For some people, becoming mindful about their eating process may be one of the best underlying strategies for weight control. Think about your last meal. Can you recall the various tastes, smells, and textures that you experienced?

Mindful Walking

To walk mindfully is to meditate while you walk. Think how much time you spend walking on a daily basis. Typically, the purpose of our walking is go somewhere, to arrive. Because of "hurry sickness" or a lack of awareness, we may miss the real journey.

While practicing mindful walking at Thich Nhat Hanh's Plum Village retreat, I recall reading a sign on one of the walking paths which read: "Walking from here to here." The purpose of walking meditation is to go nowhere. The purpose is to walk and enjoy the walk. I suspect this approach is as different for most people as it has been for me. Recalling hikes and walks in the past, I believe my main purpose was typically to arrive, and when I was walking with another person, I wanted to arrive first!

In learning to walk mindfully, develop a slow process of focusing on the *activity* and not the *destination.*

Mindful Walking Process

1. Recall your purpose in this moment: **to walk.**

2. Stop and observe: where is my awareness or attention?

3. Become aware of your breathing. Focus on the in-breath and the out-breath.

4. Begin walking with your left foot, and while breathing in say, "In." As your right foot moves forward, breathe out and say, "Out." Vary your pace and breathing to suit your needs and the environment.

5. As your mind wanders, bring your awareness/attention back to the moment by breathing in and breathing out as you walk.

Note: When walking indoors, your pace will be slower, usually one or two steps for each in-breath and the same for each out-breath. Outdoors, coordinate your breathing with your steps. You may find that three or four steps per in-breath and out-breath may be suitable for you. Using the words, "In, in, in, out, out, out," can help you to stay focused.

As you have read this section and possibly practiced mindful walking, you may think that this process is rather rigid or sterile. What about the beauty that you see along the way? What about the trees, flowers, insects, sky, and wind? To enjoy the walk, take time to focus on the beauty along the way. Stop, pause, enjoy each scene, sound, smell, and experience the journey. Breathe! Continue your focus on walking.

Recently, on a hike with my son to a beautiful mountain peak, we talked all the way to the top: one solid hour of walking and talking. He decided that on the way down we would walk without talking, "mindful walking." As we reflected on the hike an hour later, we both commented on how we became closer as father and son as we shared thoughts and feelings as we walked up the mountain. We also recognized how many more flowers and birds we saw and how many sounds we heard on the way down. The journey up the mountain created moments of intimacy with a father and son. The journey down the mountain created intimacy with father, son, mountain, and nature.

Reflections

❖　❖　❖　❖　❖　❖　❖

To eat mindfully, pay close attention to each bite.
—Daniel Goleman and Tara Bennett-Goleman

What is the use of planning to be able to eat next week,
unless I can really enjoy the meals when they come?
If I am so busy planning how to eat next week that
I cannot fully enjoy what I am eating now,
I will be in the same predicament when
next week's meals become now.
—Allan Watts

We develop this sense of interconnectedness by acknowledging
all that is eaten in its original form: envisioning the wheat that
comprises the bread, the milk of the cow, the pod of the pea.
The ocean of fish. And the sun which feeds them all. We take in
the sacred, the germ of life, like the Eucharist, in gratitude and respect.
—Stephen Levine

When was the last time you had a glass of water and really drank it?
—Thomas Merton

Each step is life, each step is joy and peace.
—Thich Nhat Hanh

It is no use walking anywhere to preach unless
our walking is our preaching.
—St. Francis of Assisi

❖ Explore ways in which mindfulness is enhanced with every step you take. When you are in a hurry, remind yourself, "Where am I going anyway?" Consider opportunities for more mindful walking. Use each step as the means of coming back to the present moment. Think about your normal walking patterns. What does your way of walking say about you? If your steps could talk, what would they say?

❖ Try an experiment using an orange. Take the orange and slowly peel it, smelling the oils that are released from the peel. Do you begin to salivate before you actually taste the orange? Carefully divide the orange into sections, and eat one small piece at a time. What do you notice as the orange touches your lips and tongue? Try this same experiment with a partner whose eyes are closed. Slowly feed the orange to your partner, and notice how all the senses are involved in the process of taste.

PART FOUR:

Maintaining a Mindful Lifestyle

In Part Four, you will:

❖ Learn ways to practice mindfulness daily

❖ Develop a process for looking deeply and gaining insight

❖ Review the meaning and practice of mindfulness

❖ Develop a personal commitment to live more mindfully

❖   ❖   ❖

The mind should be like a camera loaded with appreciation,
ready to capture in full color and in perfect focus
the essence of each beautiful moment.
—Anonymous

Make the present moment the best moment of your life.
—Thich Nhat Hanh

The only measure of success is the moment, right now.
Are we here? If we are here, our practice is perfect.
—David Cooper

Daily Practice

Becoming mindful does not happen unless you are committed first to the importance of the concept, and second, you have the discipline to go beyond the reading of this book. Discipline comes from the word "disciple," which refers to following one's love. In the same way that you cannot plan to become fit by joining a health club and then only attending occasionally, you cannot truly follow this practice without a plan or program. Mindfulness requires you to exercise the same motivation, discipline, and daily awareness consistently, until it hopefully becomes a moment-by-moment practice.

Ways to enhance the practice of mindfulness include the following suggestions:

1. Set aside time daily to practice mindful breathing. Personally, I have found early morning the best for my schedule. Find a comfortable room and create a personal space in which you sit either in a chair or on a meditation cushion. Begin with ten to twenty minutes of the basic mindfulness practice with the focus on the breath. If time permits, sessions throughout the day may be helpful.

2. Finding time each day to just "be" is one way to counteract the compulsive nature that most of us show in our constant "doing." When I was child, my mother often said, "Gerald, why don't you just sit for awhile, you are always on the go." As adults, so much of our identity is created by "doing." The "shoulds" and "oughts" often become the guiding force, and, consequently, most adults feel guilty when they are not working, and will often create additional work for themselves to avoid these guilt feelings.

    Despite early conditioning, finding time to do "nothing" each day is one way to bring balance back into a life filled with doing. Do you have a healthy balance between "being" and "doing?" Create a "lazy day" or half day or even a "lazy hour" during which you spend time "being," with no prearranged agenda. If you want to read, read. If you want to sleep, sleep. Don't think about your responsibilities or "shoulds." If you have younger children that need tending, arrange with your partner or a friend to be responsible for them. Take turns being responsible and being "lazy."

3.   Create a practice of completing personal or professional tasks each day. For example, gardening is an ongoing project that requires mindfulness to successfully complete the task. Before beginning, decide on how much work you have time to complete. Begin the task and continue until completed. When you are distracted, use the work as a source of meditation. Apply this same awareness to projects at work. For example, my work often involves writing and organizational business planning. If I "bracket" 30 minutes to write, I may set a timer and continue to write for that time period. As I am interrupted by thoughts, feelings, etc., I note the distraction and repeatedly return to the task at hand.

4.   Use mindfulness to enhance relationships. Identify several individuals who are most significant in your life and use them as reminders to be mindful. When you find your mind wandering in conversation, continue to bring your attention back to the person. Remember the best gift that you give to each person is your self.

5.   Create an environment at home and work that offers opportunities and reminders to be mindful. During my stay at Plum Village, practicing was relatively easy, since each phone call, the frequent ringing of a bell, and each meal were all invitations to pause and be mindful. At home and in the office, we can also find reminders to stop, pause, and breathe. Invitations to return to the moment are present in our own environment. A beeper sound, a phone ringing, or a microwave bell, can be used

as reminders to breathe and return to the present moment. A bell placed on the kitchen counter and rung randomly provides a reminder to stop, pause, and renew. You can pause and breathe at the first ring of the telephone. When driving out of your garage, pause and breathe as you watch the garage door slowly close.

6. Develop social support for the practice of mindfulness. Practicing mindfulness becomes easier in an office or home when other people are mindful. For example, when my wife eats mindfully, I am reminded to focus on the process of eating, rather than watching the news and reading the paper at the same time. In the work place, when several people begin to model mindfulness through their work and relationships, other colleagues are affected. Recently, a group of nurses that I worked with decided to use call bells, beepers, phone calls, and pages as reminders to briefly pause, breathe, and become mindful. This practice became the norm, and through the example of one another, the entire unit became more mindful. Imagine the healing effect that this ultimately may have on their relationships and the health of their patients.

The ultimate goal of daily practice is to create simple reminders that each moment is an opportunity to practice mindfulness.

Reflections

❖   ❖   ❖   ❖   ❖   ❖   ❖

Are we human beings or human doings?
—Anonymous

Listen, listen.
This wonderful sound brings me back to my true self.
—Thich Nhat Hanh

❖   My plan to include mindfulness in my daily schedule is:

Looking Deeply—Gaining Insight

By living in the here and now, we have an opportunity to stop, observe, and "look deeply" at our thinking, sensing, feeling, and experiencing. When we do so, every encounter has profound meaning. Each person we meet and every action we take offers an opportunity for growth and insight.

As your practice of daily mindfulness progresses, you will begin to gain insights regarding the meaning behind your thoughts, sensations, feelings and experiences.

In the process of "looking deeply," you begin to live your life in a more insightful rather than robotic way. Stopping to explore thoughts, feelings, sensations, and bodily experiences offers an individual one of the deepest forms of therapy. Whenever I have been able to stop, find a quiet environment, and retreat into myself, profound changes take place. Some of my best insights have come from quiet walks along the ocean, hiking in the mountains, and even in my own quiet space at home. Away from the everyday sounds of television, radio, stereos, traffic, and people, you can discover a new relationship with yourself. Most people are literally afraid of this kind of quiet, since they have not developed a way to communicate with self. Mindfulness is a process that, offers us a technique for "witnessing" those aspects of life which create fear.

When appropriate, take some time to engage in the following process.

1. Look deeply at a thought you are experiencing. Be with the thought.
    Why this thought? What does it mean? Why am I focused on this particular thought?

2. Look deeply at a feeling you are experiencing. Be with the feeling.
   If the feeling could talk, what would it say to you?

3. Look deeply at one sensation in your body. Be with the sensation.
   If your body could talk, what would it say?

4. Look deeply at a person you love. Accept this person completely in this moment.
   What is it that you really value in this individual?

5. Overall, **stop** and **observe** and **look deeply** at your moment-by-moment behavior. Everyday activities, such as eating, speaking, and working, often take place without thought or consideration. In the process of *looking deeply,* you will begin to see the interconnection between every action. As you begin to slow down and practice this process, you are more likely to make positive health decisions that affect not only yourself but literally everyone in the world.

The ultimate challenge of practicing mindfulness is to gain insights moment by moment that will impact your growth and ultimately have an impact on everyone in your immediate and extended environment. While at Plum Village, we were reminded by Thich Nhat Hanh that our individual practice of being mindful has an effect on everyone. As you look deeply, it becomes clear that "no man is an island." Every action of mine has a profound impact on those around me, and literally the whole universe.

Through this practice, I have become more conscious of the impact that I have on the environment. I am more likely to recycle, use fewer products that may create a negative impact, and walk when possible. Since embracing the practice of mindfulness, I have literally changed my diet, stopped drinking alcoholic beverages, and have become more aware of living simply. All of these lifestyle changes were made internally after looking deeply at the potential consequence of each of my behaviors. When asked, "What is the greatest message we can leave for others?" Gandhi said simply, "My life is my message."

Reflections

❖   ❖   ❖   ❖   ❖   ❖   ❖

Looking deeply at life as it is in the very here and now, the practitioner dwells in stability and freedom.
—Thich Nhat Hanh

Understanding is the fruit of looking deeply.
—Thich Nhat Hanh

❖   In what ways can I look more deeply today?

What's it all about?
Moment by Moment

On a recent trip to Hawaii, I met a playwright who had written numerous Broadway and Hollywood productions. While having coffee together, I asked him if he had any "secrets" regarding writing. He replied, "People go to a play, movie, or read books with the hope of getting at least one thought or inspiration. People usually ask their friends, 'What was it all about?'" In his writing, he hoped to leave his readers with one message that would add to their lives.

So what is mindfulness all about?

Mindfulness ...

❖ Is experiencing the body, mind, and spirit in the same place at the same time. It is an awareness of the present moment and your activity in that moment.

❖ Helps you to reduce stress, increase productivity, and enhance relationships, and it can be the basis of creating joy in life.

❖ Incorporates an awareness of breathing as the vehicle used to call attention to the present moment, renew the body, and quiet the mind.

❖ Is a process of ...

1. Knowing your purpose.

2. Being aware of your thinking, sensing, feeling, and bodily experiences.

3. Bringing your awareness/attention back to the moment and your purpose by breathing in and breathing out.

❖ Is a practice that teaches one to "witness" rather than become attached: thoughts are thoughts, and feelings are simply feelings.

❖ Is practiced moment by moment.

In the space to the right, begin a list of the activities you engage in routinely, such as getting up in the morning, eating breakfast, taking a shower, driving to work, talking to friends, exercising, doing house or yard work, working, and preparing to go to bed.

Be as specific as possible in detailing the activities you engage in on a routine basis. Following each activity, describe specific ways you will become more mindful during that activity.

Examples:

ROUTINE ACTIVITY
MINDFUL ACTIVITY

1. EATING BREAKFAST
   I will eat slowly and enjoy the food.
   I will not watch television or read the paper as I eat.

2. DRIVING TO WORK
   I will use traffic jams as an opportunity to practice breathing and drive mindfully.

ROUTINE ACTIVITY / Mindful Activity:

1.

2.

3.

4.

5.

Reflections

❖　❖　❖　❖　❖　❖　❖

Each day in life is training. Training for myself.
Living each moment, equal to anything, ready for everything.
I am active. I am this Moment. My future is here and now.
For if I cannot endure today, when and where will I?
—Soen Ozeki

Shadows of the past are vague, and the future is too
distant to come into focus. Now is brightly illuminated and richly colored.
Today I will remember to keep my mind in the present.
Now is all I have. Now is all anyone has.
—Judith Garrison

Yesterday is but a dream, tomorrow is but a vision.
But today well-lived makes every yesterday a dream of happiness,
and every tomorrow a vision of hope. Look well, therefore, to this day.
—Sanskrit proverb

The gift of life with all its joy and splendor is in the moment at hand.
Now it is ours to relish and enjoy; now it is ours to cherish
and to hold, but only for the moment.
—Adolfo Quezada

❖　For me, this book is about...

Bibliography

Andrews, Frank. *The Art and Practice of Loving.* Los Angeles: Jeremy P. Tarcher, Inc., 1991.

Borysenko, J. *Minding the Body, Mending the Mind.* Reading, Mass.: Addison Wesley, 1987.

Brandon, David. *Zen in the Art of Helping.* New York: Arakana, 1990.

Carlson, Richard and Benjamin Shield. *Healers on Healing.* Los Angeles: Jeremy P. Tarcher, Inc., 1989.

Cooper, David A. , *The Heart of Stillness,* NewYork: Bell Tower, 1992.

—————, *Silence, Simplicity, and Solitude.* New York: Bell Tower, 1992.

Csikszentmihalyi, Mihaly. *Flow: The Psychology of Optimal Experience.* New York: Harper & Row, 1990.

Cummings, Charles. *The Mystery of the Ordinary.* New York: Harper & Row, 1982.

Dass, Ram. *Be Here Now.* New York: Crown, 1971.

DeMello, Anthony. *Sadhana: A Way To God.* New York: Doubleday, 1984.

Fields, Rick, et al. *Chop Wood, Carry Water.* Los Angeles: Jeremy Tarcher, Inc., 1984.

Goldstein, Joseph. *The Experience of Insight: A Natural Unfolding.* Santa Cruz: Unity Press, 1987.

—————, and Jack Kornfield. *Seeking the Heart of Wisdom: The Path of Insight Meditation.* Boston: Shambhala, 1987.

Goleman, Daniel and Tara Bennett-Goleman. *The Meditative Mind: The Varieties of Meditative Experience.* Los Angeles: Jeremy Tarcher, Inc., 1988.

Hanh, Thich Nhat. *Being Peace.* Berkeley: Parallax Press, 1987.

——————. *Breathe! You Are Alive.* Berkeley: Parallax Press, 1988.

——————. *A Guide to Walking Meditation.* Nyack, New York: Fellowship of Reconciliation, 1985.

——————. *The Miracle of Mindfulness.* New York: Beacon Press, 1976.

——————. *Our Appointment With Life.* Berkeley: Parallax Press, 1990.

——————. *Peace is Every Step.* New York: Bantam Books, 1991.

——————. *Present Moment, Wonderful Moment.* Berkeley: Parallax Press, 1990.

——————. *The Sun, My Heart.* Berkeley: Parallax Press, 1988.

Johnson, Spencer. *Precious Present.* New York: Doubleday, 1984.

Kabat-Zinn, Jon. *Full Catastrophe Living.* New York: Delacorte Press, 1990.

Kavanaugh, James. *Search.* San Francisco: Harper & Row, 1985.

Keating, Thomas. *Open Mind, Open Heart.* Rockport, Mass.:, 1991.

Kornfield, Jack and Paul Breitzer. *A Still Forest Pool.* Wheaton, Ill.: Theosophical Publishing House, 1985.

Langer, Ellen. *Mindfulness.* Reading, Mass.: Addison Wesley, 1989.

Levine, Stephen. *A Gradual Awakening.* New York: Anchor-Doubleday, 1979.

Levine, Stephen. *Guided Meditations, Explorations, and Healing.* New York: Anchor, 1991.

Pennington, Basil. *Centered Living.* New York: Image, 1986.

Reid, Clyde. *Celebrate the Temporary.* New York: Harper & Row, 1972.

Sinetar, Marsha. *Do What You Love, the Money Will Follow.* New York: Paulist Press, 1987.

Suzuki, Shunryu. *Zen Mind, Beginner's Mind.* New York: Weatherhill, 1986.

Valles, Carlos G. *Courage to Be Myself.* New York: Doubleday, 1989.

Wilber, Ken. *Grace and Grit.* Boston: Shambhala, 1991.

——————. *No Boundaries.* Boston: Shambhala, 1985.

❖   ❖   ❖

For information regarding books by Thich Nhat Hanh, contact:

Parallax Press
P.O. Box 7355
Berkeley, California 94707

❖   ❖   ❖

To subscribe to the *Mindfulness Bell*,
a quarterly publication dedicated to mindful living, contact:

Community of Mindful Living
P.O. Box 7355
Berkeley, California 94707

About the Author

Jerry Braza, Ph.D. has facilitated workshops for over 5,000 health professionals, including nurses, social workers, psychologists, doctors, and allied health professionals nationwide. His background includes over 20 years experience as a university professor with multi-disciplinary training in health, management, and psychology. Dr. Braza created and facilitates nationwide *Healing the Healer: A Workshop for Those Who Care.* During the past ten years, he has developed a personal and theoretical understanding of Mindfulness through his experience and training with leaders in the field, including Thich Nhat Hanh, a nominee for the Nobel Peace Prize. He recently created the *Mindfulness Training Program* to assist individuals with managing stress, enhancing their relationships, becoming more productive, and living more fully.

Healing Resources was created by Jerry and Kathleen Braza to offer programs for caregivers. Kathleen, a certified thanatologist (grief specialist), offers programs on grief, loss, and healing.

For additional information regarding programs, seminars, or newsletters, contact:

Healing Resources

P.O. Box 9478
Salt Lake City, Utah 84109
(801) 484-8220
or
1-800-473-HEAL